I WASN'T KIDDING!

Or
How To Commit Suicide
So They'll <u>Never</u> Forget

A

for

ıl ı

one

G000016666

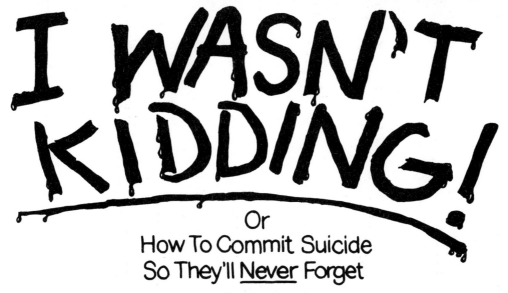

I WASN'T KIDDING!

Or
How To Commit Suicide
So They'll Never Forget

by **Andrew Christie**
and **Karen Heuler**

ANGUS
& ROBERTSON
PUBLISHERS

ANGUS & ROBERTSON PUBLISHERS

Unit 4, Eden Park, 31 Waterloo Road,
North Ryde, NSW, Australia 2113
and
16 Golden Square, London W1R 4BN,
United Kingdom

First published in Australia by
Angus & Robertson Publishers in 1985
First published in the United Kingdom
by Angus & Robertson (UK) Ltd in 1985
This edition published by arrangement
with Ballantine Books, a division of
Random House, Inc.

National Library of Australia
Cataloguing-in-publication data.

Christie, Andrew.
    I wasn't kidding, or, How to commit
    suicide so they'll never forget.
    ISBN 0 207 15057 5.

    1. American wit and humor, Pictorial.
    2. Suicide — Caricatures and cartoons.
    I. Heuler, Karen. II. Title.
    III. Title: How to commit suicide so
    they'll never forget.

741.5'973

Printed in the United Kingdom

With special thanks to our good friend Ed Bell
for all his help and ideas

Why Did You Pick Up This Book?

Greetings, traveler. Feeling tired, run down, weary of life and all its strategies? Have you often wondered why go on, why put up with it all? Do you find yourself lingering on bridges, on rooftops, at crosswalks and rivers? Are you irritated when someone says, "Have a nice day"?

Of course you are. But you don't have to be. There's something you can do to change your life. Permanently. Without criticism and without expense.

Has getting ahead lost its glitter? Is getting rich unreal? Becoming famous unlikely? Have you noticed that what you really want is to get even? Isn't that it? Things are not going well—in fact, they haven't been going well for quite some time—and you know that they never will. Because someone or something out there has it in for you.

We know *you're* not the problem. As a famous author once said, "I am only one and they are all." It's the "all" part of it that's dragging you down.

What can you do about it? Why should you spend thousands to go to a therapist to find out how wrong you've been all your life? You're the only one who really understands how unique and intractable your problems are. Sure, *maybe* you can read a book that can show you how to win back your lover, get a new job, pay back the funds you've embezzled or find a meaning in life. Maybe. But be honest—how often does that happen in the real world? No, let's face it, all too frequently life just doesn't get any better. Depression is a valid response to the world and to life, and no one should be counseled to fight it. In fact, it may be the best thing that *ever* happened to you—*if you act on it while there's still time*. That's what this book is about: how to improve your life in the most meaningful way. We want to get you to encourage your natural self-expression. Don't hold back any longer; give in to your impulses—but do it in a creative way.

Let's Consider Some Advantages

Think about what it will be like: You'll never have to pay taxes, go on a diet, take public transportation, go to a dentist or put up with rude waiters ever again. Sound good? You won't have to work, wake up to an alarm clock, suffer gastrointestinal distress or pay off your outstanding debts. All that will be over. Never again!

And if you hurry now you can be the first on your block. For the very first time you'll have instant popularity—or at the very least, celebrity.

Are you ready for this book? Let's put it in perspective. If you're the kind of person no one thinks about, who doesn't get invited out to dinner unless someone else cancels and you're taken so much for granted that your miseries are neighborhood jokes, if it's finally dawned on you that you're too old to be in the Olympics, too dumb to win the Nobel Prize and too dull to appear on Johnny Carson, what's stopping you? Could it be you're too considerate?

A Matter of Impact—Get Them Where It Hurts

You've spent your life taking care of other people—and for what? So they could drive you crazy? And now you're wondering if you have the right to take a long, permanent rest—or if that desire means you're evil and selfish and uncaring.

Why think that? If the people around you are driving you to contemplate bridges, why should you spare their feelings?

Have they ever spared yours?

If you've had enough, if you're frustrated, mad as hell and considering ending it all, take comfort in the knowledge that countless thousands have preceded you on this controversial road. And, if you choose the ultimate solution, do yourself a favor—make it count. Give 'em hell and do it so they'll never forget it!

You won't regret your decision. We've never met anyone who did.

Personal Achievement, Domestic Tranquillity, Modern Romance and Everyday Life

Why does everyone ignore you?
Why do the children put garlic in your coffee?
Where was your husband last night?
Why does everything keep breaking down?
Where did all these bills come from?
When was the last time you had any fun?
Where's your best friend?
Do you remember what good sex was like?
Does anyone think you're *too* thin?

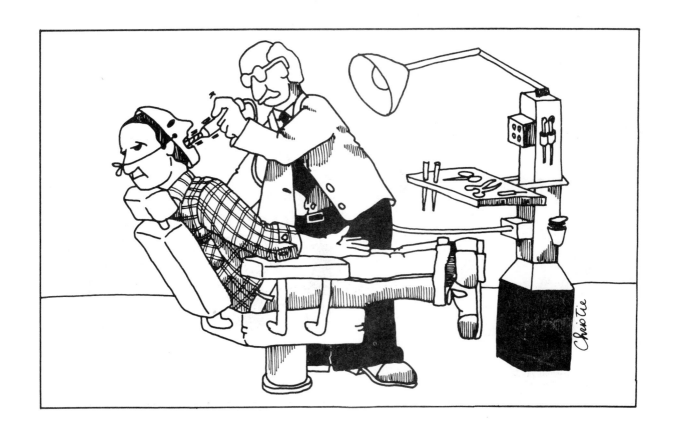

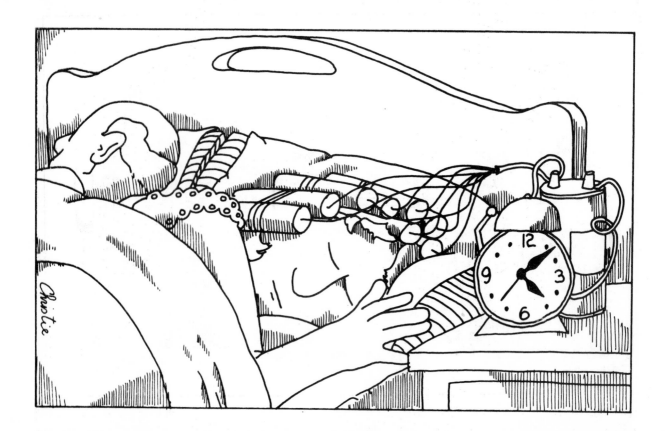

Christie

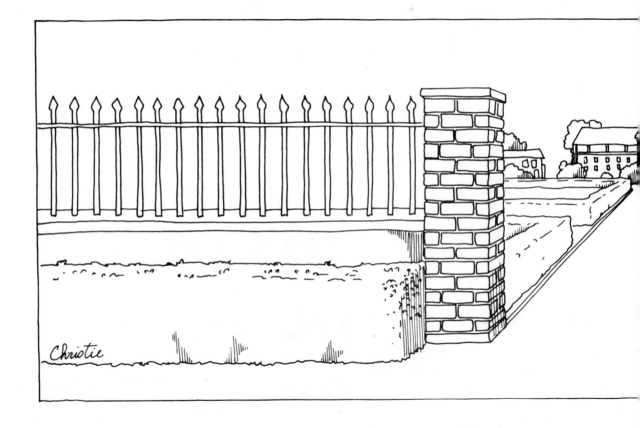

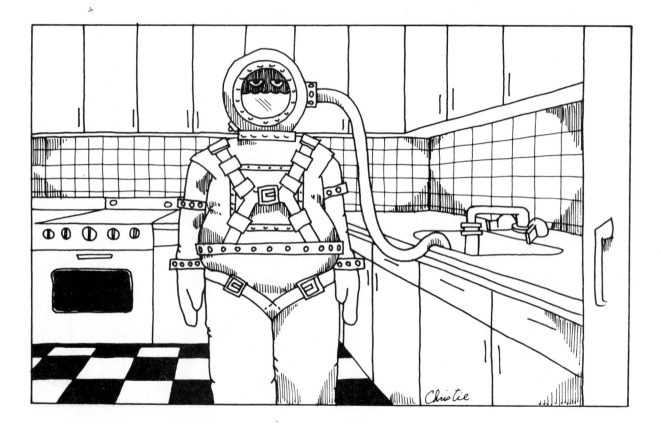

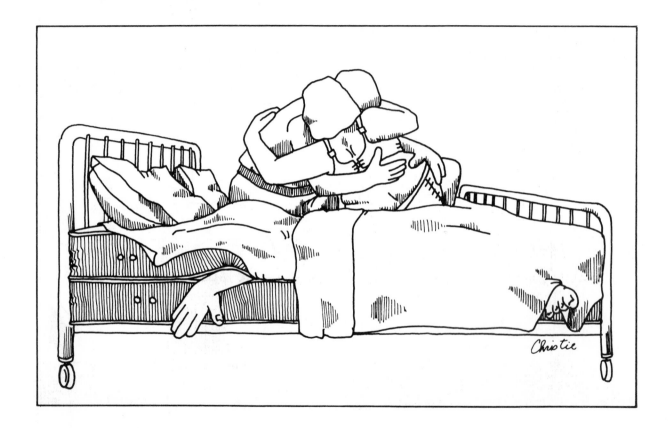

Christie

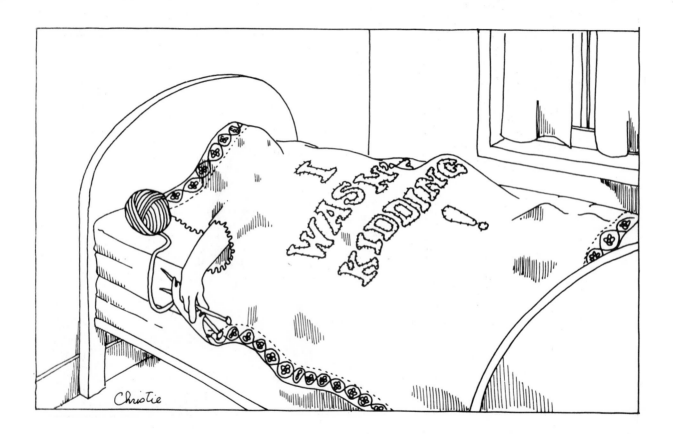

Christie

Sports, Games and Other Activities

Do you seriously believe you could
win if you tried harder?

Do people let you win just to get it
over with?

Did the person with the short straw
draw you as their partner?

Do they refer to you as the dummy in
games other than bridge?

Are you an offensive player on and off
the field?

Do you have trouble knowing when
the game is over?

When was the last time you boasted
about how you scored?

Is "sudden death" your favorite part
of any game?

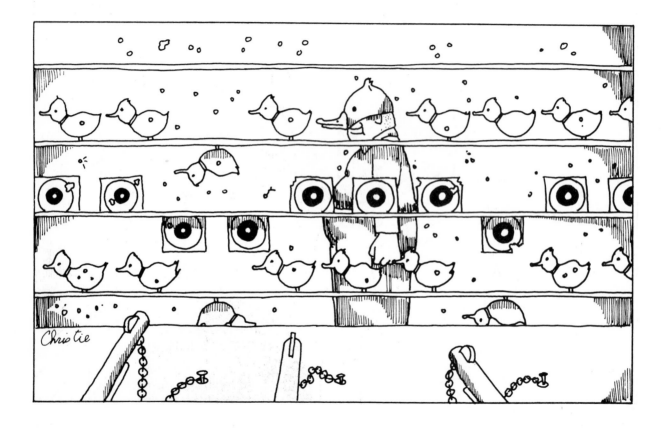

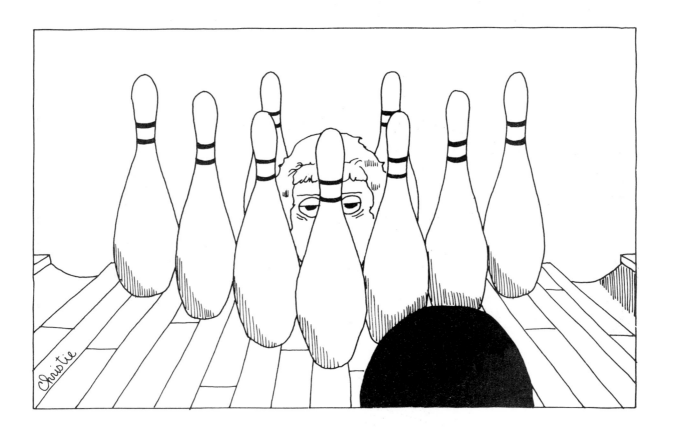

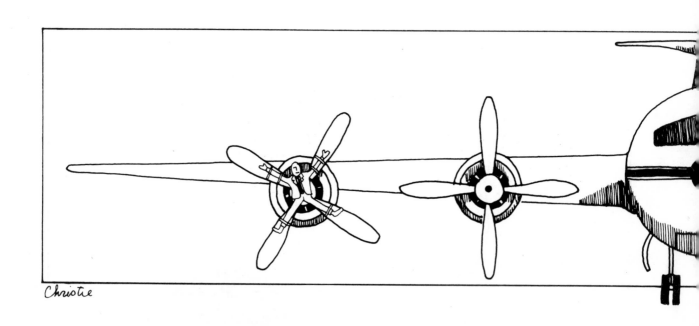

Christie

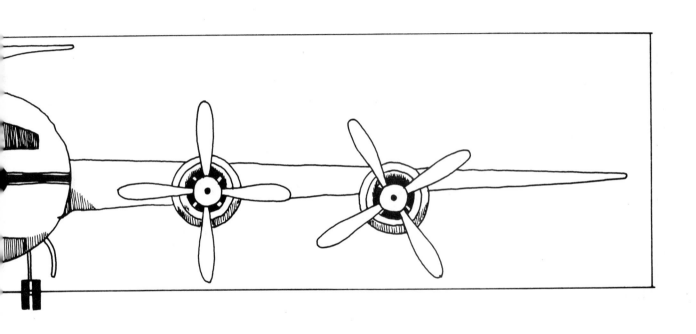

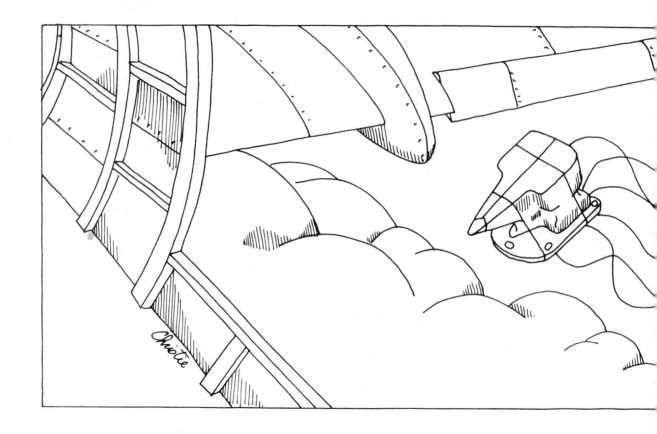

Job Satisfaction

How long can you wait for that
promotion?
Why is your office so small?
Who decided you had to work all
your life?
How come you're so smart but *they*
have all the power?
Why don't you have a corner office?
Why has your boss been talking about
computers lately?
Has anyone admired you in the past
ten years?

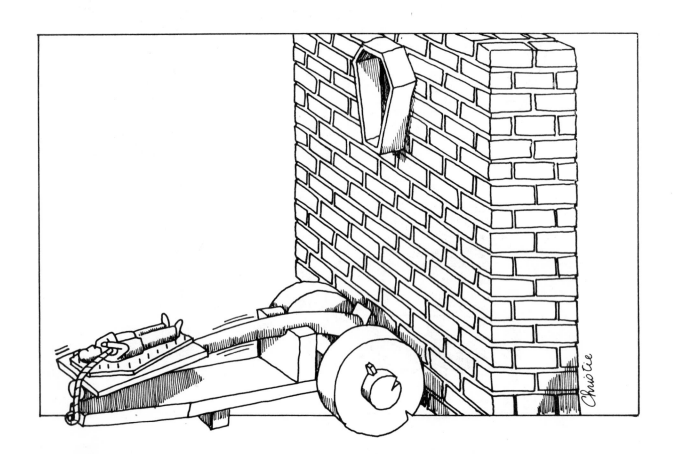

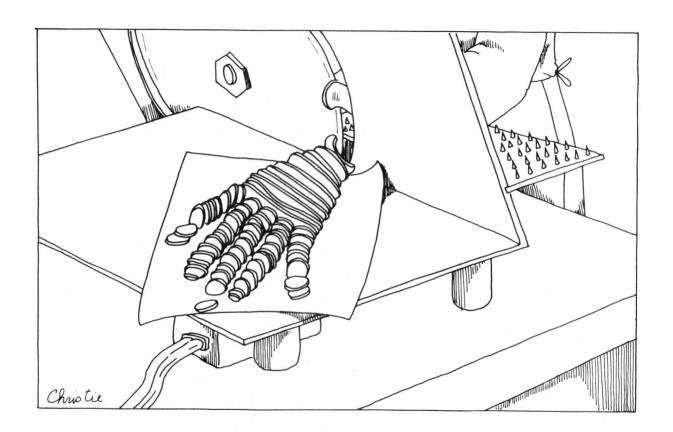

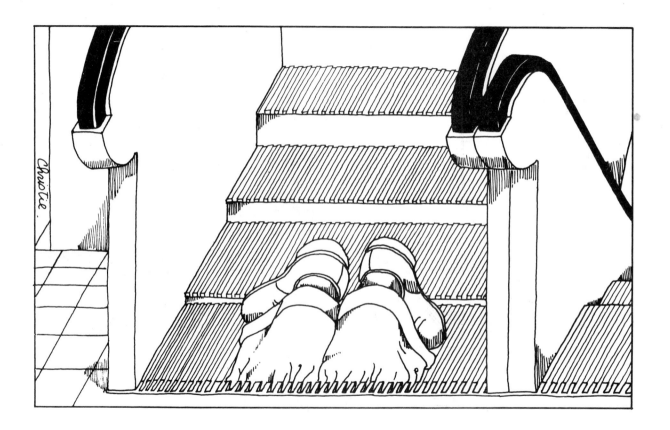

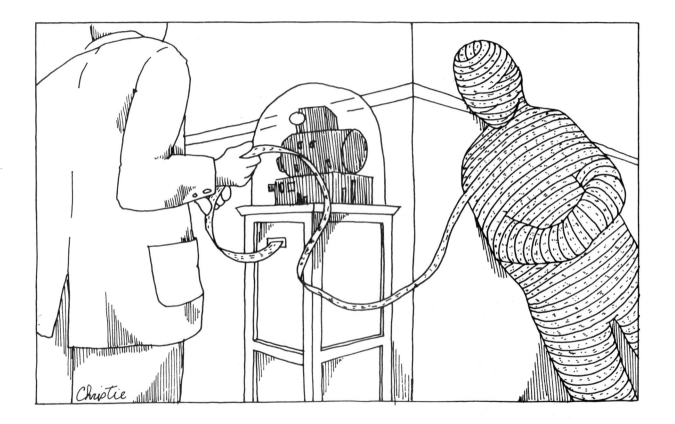

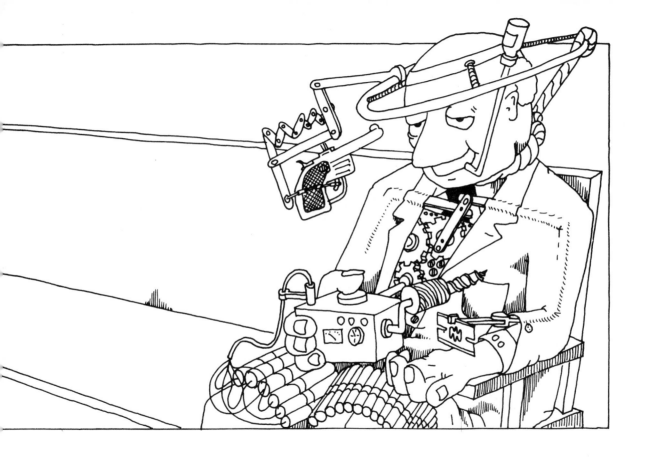

Special Occasions

When was the last time you won at
 anything?
Do you give lousy parties?
Are you older than you ever thought
 you'd be?
Are you the last to be picked for any
 group activity, including lines?
Are the only Valentine cards you get
 forgeries?
Are you always celebrating something
 for someone else?
Do you get used presents for
 Christmas?

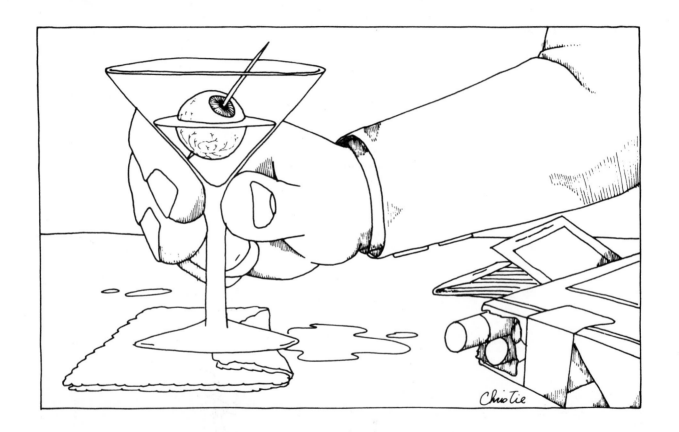

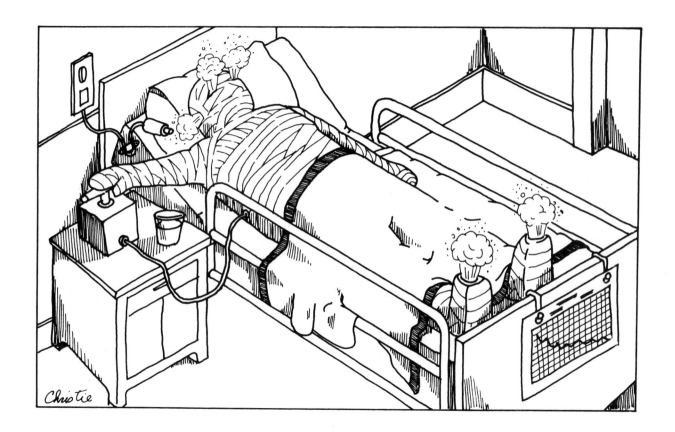

A Checklist for Candidates

You've given this book your undivided attention, but you're still not sure what to answer when someone asks, "how are you?" We've prepared this questionnaire in order to provide you with some method of understanding yourself. All you have to do is mark the box that most closely approximates your response to the questions asked. Each box has a number; at the end of the test, add up your score and find out how you're feeling.

	Never	Once	Sometimes	Often
Score:	1	2	3	4
1. Do you ride in cars, trains, buses or planes?	☐	☐	☐	☐
2. During the course of a week, do you go outside your home or apartment?	☐	☐	☐	☐
3. Would you like to live in a computerized society?	☐	☐	☐	☐
4. The latest studies have shown that people who exercise are obsessed with health and death. Do you do any form of exercise (including walking?)	☐	☐	☐	☐
5. Do you eat foods such as pizza, charcoal-grilled steaks or burgers or french fries?	☐	☐	☐	☐
6. Do you drink coffee or alcohol?	☐	☐	☐	☐
7. Is your life a routine?	☐	☐	☐	☐
8. Are you afraid of getting a part of your anatomy stuck in mechanical objects with gears?	☐	☐	☐	☐
9. Do you fantasize about "getting away" to a "foreign land" or "island"?	☐	☐	☐	☐
10. Do you feel alone in the world?	☐	☐	☐	☐

	Never	Once	Sometimes	Often
Score:	1	2	3	4
11. Do you feel the world is closing in on you?	☐	☐	☐	☐
12. Have you made a will?	☐	☐	☐	☐
13. Do you watch more than four hours of TV each night?	☐	☐	☐	☐
14. Do you see the same movie more than once?	☐	☐	☐	☐
15. Do you ever feel "blue"?	☐	☐	☐	☐
16. In any given hour, do you feel like quitting your job?	☐	☐	☐	☐
17. Are you drawn to sensational books, newspapers or movies?	☐	☐	☐	☐
18. Are you kind-hearted?	☐	☐	☐	☐
19. Are you afraid of children?	☐	☐	☐	☐
20. Do you smoke cigarettes? (double points on this!)	☐	☐	☐	☐
21. Do you know the exact location of the nearest bridge?	☐	☐	☐	☐
22. Do you have a roach and/or pest problem in your home?	☐	☐	☐	☐

	Never	Once	Sometimes	Often
Score:	1	2	3	4
23. When was the Spanish Armada defeated?	☐	☐	☐	☐
24. Do your friends tell you you're a happy person?	☐	☐	☐	☐
25. Does it take you more than thirty minutes to travel to work?	☐	☐	☐	☐
26. Do you have a telephone?	☐	☐	☐	☐
27. Do you give cocktail parties?	☐	☐	☐	☐
28. Do you bowl or do any sport well?	☐	☐	☐	☐
29. Do you pay your bills on time?	☐	☐	☐	☐
30. Do you have trouble starting your car, especially in winter?	☐	☐	☐	☐
31. Do you keep at least one sharp knife in your home?	☐	☐	☐	☐
32. Do you understand the economy?	☐	☐	☐	☐
33. Do you get paper cuts?	☐	☐	☐	☐
34. In a thunderstorm, do you count between a flash of lightning and a peal of thunder?	☐	☐	☐	☐
35. Do you use elevators?	☐	☐	☐	☐

		Never	Once	Sometimes	Often
	Score:	1	2	3	4
36. Do your teeth hurt?		☐	☐	☐	☐
37. Are you afraid of anything?		☐	☐	☐	☐
38. Do you like spiders?		☐	☐	☐	☐
39. Are some of your clothes too large and some too small?		☐	☐	☐	☐
40. Have you ever been particularly fond of Thursdays?		☐	☐	☐	☐
41. Do you wish you were younger or had more hair or didn't have gray hair?		☐	☐	☐	☐
42. Do you ever feel you were happier ten years ago?		☐	☐	☐	☐
43. How many pets do you have?		☐	☐	☐	☐
44. What kind(s) is(are) it(they)?		☐	☐	☐	☐
45. Now add up your score:		———	———	———	———

0— 50	Forget it. You're already dead.
50— 60	You're completely happy and you were thinking of someone else when you picked up this book.
60—100	Few people are totally honest when they take a test like this. Are you holding something back? Are you sure you answered Nos. 13, 25, and 37 accurately? Why are you lying?
100—200	Congratulations. You're very depressed. If this book was a gift, thank the person who gave it to you and then say goodbye.

ABOUT THE AUTHORS

Andrew Christie is an illustrator and graphic designer and a past recipient of the Desi Award for graphic design. **Karen Heuler** is a writer. Both authors live in New York City. This is their first book.